BBC Children in Need

Pudsey
Annual

Hello and welcome to the very first Pudsey Annual!

It's been a privilege and a pleasure to have been involved with BBC Children in Need since the very beginning 30 years ago. But this, our first annual, I think is a great idea. Crammed full of fun stories, games and activities, I'm sure it will also give you lots of exciting fundraising ideas too!

There are tons of great things for you to do. My favourite is a terrific dot-to-dot Pudsey on page 37! Or, if you like making tasty treats there are some great cake recipes you can try out on page 48 - don't forget to ask an adult to help you out though. We don't want Pudsey to get the blame for cake mixture all over the kitchen! Maybe you could even sell your cakes to friends and family afterwards to help raise some money. I know lots of children who already do. And remember, it doesn't matter how much or how little you raise. Every penny counts.

Also, don't forget to keep an eye out for some of our famous friends, including the star of the show - Pudsey! All of them have done something for BBC Children in Need - but what will you do? If you've helped in the past, well done, please help us again. If this is your first time, this book can show you how.

Remember, if you do any fundraising you'll be helping us make other children all over the country who are unhappy smile again. And I know you'll have fun doing it. Thank you.

Terry Wogan

This book belongs to

Adam

Kenny

Contents

Do Something Different

Pudsey loves **BBC Children in Need**, because it's about helping children right here, in the UK.

He gets his famous friends together to help out. After all, what other cuddly bear has the last of the Time Lords or pop stars like McFly as his friends?

Pudsey smiles with the glamorous Estelle to raise awareness about the kids in the UK that need your help.

Pudsey lets these guys get on with the show, because they like to talk. A lot.

Then while everyone is getting ready for the big television programme, he's out visiting the amazing people who help raise money for **BBC Children in Need.**

He likes to visit schools.

This is Pudsey with the Carmarthenshire School Dragon. Too many treats from the cake sale, but it was for a good cause!

He likes to visit families.

He likes to coach his friends at the British Transplant Games.

He likes to have a good cuddle.

And he likes to say thank you for helping BBC Children in Need.

Last year, you helped raise £36 million pounds to help support hundreds of projects across the UK. The money you raise makes a real difference to the lives of thousands of disadvantaged children and young people in the UK. Whatever you do for BBC Children in Need, be creative! And silly too. Just Do Something Different.

Fundraising Game

All you need to play is a dice, some coloured counters and your friends. Take it in turns to roll the dice and move the number of spaces it tells you to, following any instructions you land on. Who will be the first to win and raise £50?

£5

£6

£4

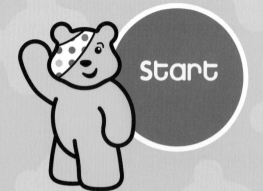

Start

£1

£2

Move back £2

You sleep through your alarm and are late for a school fundraising event.

£35

£36

£37

Move Forward £3

£39

£34

You put on a play with your friends to raise money.

£40

£33

You talk during a sponsored silence.

£41

£42

£32

£31

Move back £4

£29

£28

£27

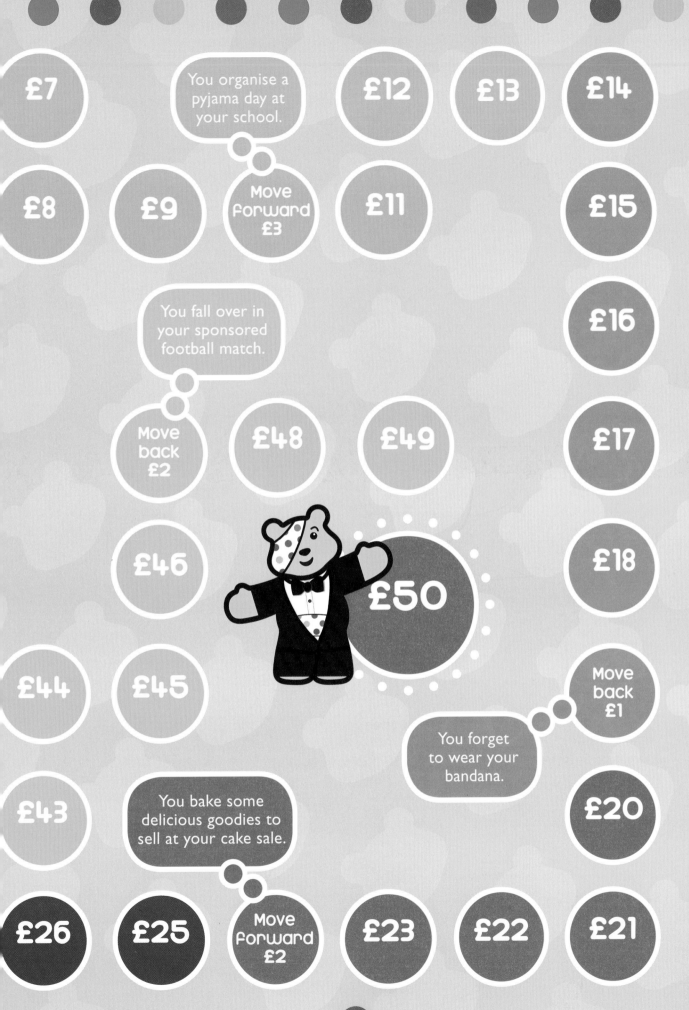

Be Different

Look at the pictures of Pudsey. One picture in each row is different from the others. Can you see which one it is?

Word Search

Can you find all of the words in Pudsey's word search?

```
C H A N G E E J L E L T B A C
A I L R E U Q K W K D R E B I
C E L E B R I T I E S T H U C
H A L T E N U K G L M Z D D I
A H I M P R O V E S O O I S E
R S T E A U L I K N L S N U K
I O I G A N A G F C V I O E G
T H L I N U H W A T M L E Y
Y R M O L R D T P Y G P Y S F
M F I L R V M R U O K R I T U
E O A B H E L P I N G O N I N
T O K A L E A N U G H V A N D
O S P O N S O R S E O E E Y I
T U D O N A T I O N J N R N N
C H I L D R E N P U D S E Y G
```

BBC   Donation   Money
Celebrities   Funding   Pudsey
Change   Helping   Sponsors
Charity   Improve   Silly
Children

13

Follow the Path

Pudsey doesn't know which path to follow to reach his friend. Can you help him?

Match the Pudseys

What a lot of Pudseys! Can you match the bears that are the same?

1 . . . . 2 ヨ . . 3 A. . 4 C . . 5 . . . .

6 . . . . 7 . . . . 8 . . . . 9 B . . 10 D . .

A ✓ B ✓ C ✓ D ✓ E ✓

F G H I J

The Gingerbread Man

One day, an old lady decided she
needed a friend, so she bought some flour,
some sugar, some butter and some ginger
and she baked herself a gingerbread man.
She gave him chocolate drops for eyes and
raisins for buttons. "You will make a fine
friend for me," she said.

When the gingerbread man was cooked,
the old lady opened the oven door. But
before she could lift him out he had
jumped onto the floor and run away!
The old lady followed him as quickly as she could.
As she ran, she heard him call out, "Run, run, as fast as
you can, you can't catch me, I'm the gingerbread man!"

Pudsey loves a good story.
How about you?

16

The gingerbread man ran into a field where there was a hungry cow.
"I think I'll eat that gingerbread man up!" he said. But the gingerbread man kept
on running and called back, "Run, run, as fast as you can, you can't catch me,
I'm the gingerbread man!"

Next, the gingerbread man ran into a field where there was a hungry horse.
"I think I'll eat that gingerbread man up!" he said.

But the gingerbread man kept on running and called back,
"Run, run, as fast as you can, you can't catch me, I'm the gingerbread man!"

Soon, the gingerbread man came to a wood, where there was a hungry fox.
"I think I'll eat that gingerbread man up!" he said. But the gingerbread man kept on running and called back, "Run, run, as fast as you can, you can't catch me, I'm the gingerbread man!"
And the fox DID run as fast as he could.

They came to a hedge and the fox smiled. Now the gingerbread man would be trapped! But the gingerbread man saw a tiny hole, right at the bottom, and jumped through it. The hole was far too small for the furious fox, and all he could do was peep through at the gingerbread man, safe on the other side, laughing and singing, "Run, run, as fast as you can. You can't catch me, I'm the gingerbread man!"

Gingerbread People

Ingredients

- 50g/2oz butter or margarine
- 50g/2oz golden caster sugar
- 100g/3½ oz golden syrup
- 1 heaped teaspoon ground ginger
- 200g/7oz self-raising flour

- icing pens
- raisins

You will also need:
- gingerbread people-shaped cutters

Bake For BBC Children in Need

1. Ask your grown-up helper to pre-heat the oven to 180C/350F/Gas mark 4. Lightly grease a baking tray.

2. Put the butter or margarine, sugar and syrup in a saucepan. Ask your grown-up helper to heat it gently until the sugar has dissolved. Do not allow the mixture to boil.

3. Take the pan off the heat and pour the mixture into a bowl. Stir in the ginger and flour until you have smooth dough. Allow it to cool for thirty minutes.

4. Sprinkle a little flour on a clean work surface and roll out the dough to about ½ inch thick.

5. Use your cutters to cut out gingerbread people. Lift them carefully with a spatula onto the baking tray.

6. Ask your grown-up helper to place them in the oven for about ten minutes.

7. Let them cool on a wire rack, then decorate with the icing pens. Use the raisins for eyes and buttons.

Gingerbread Dress·up

Use your crayons to help Pudsey
decorate this gingerbread man.

Draw for
Children in Need

Wrap Stars

Wrap For Children in Need

Pudsey likes to make cakes and biscuits to give to his friends as presents. They always look so much nicer when they are in pretty boxes. Follow the steps below to make gift boxes for your cakes and biscuits.

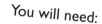

You will need:
- some big sheets of coloured paper
- a potato and a carrot
- some thick poster paints
- a paintbrush
- a bit of grown-up help

1 Ask a grown-up to cut the potato and carrot in half. Put the carrot aside and paint one of the flat faces of the potato.

2 Place the painted side of the potato down onto the paper and press firmly. Then lift off, leaving a printed coloured shape. Repeat several times. Then do the same thing using the other half of the potato and a different colour.

3 When you have finished using the potato, continue printing with the two halves of the carrot. Use other colours if you have them — but it doesn't matter if you don't. The carrot will give a different shape from the potato.

4 Leave the paint to dry. Then use your colourful home-made paper to wrap up presents for your family and friends.

Spot the Difference

There are five differences between the two pictures of Pudsey – can you spot them all?

Watch Something Different

The programmes on the **BBC** are so excited about helping Pudsey that they got all mixed up! Can you draw a line between the name and picture of the TV programme?

Saturday Kitchen

Strictly Come Dancing

Casualty

Doctor Who

Match of the Day

Colour By Numbers

Colour in the picture of Pudsey. Follow the
numbers to see which colours to use.

1 red   2 yellow   3 blue   4 green   5 brown

Pudsey Sudoku

Make sure each box, each line across and each line down have every picture of Pudsey once. You can cut out the counters at the bottom of the page to help.

Hansel and Gretel

Hansel and Gretel lived with their father and stepmother in a little house by a wood. They were very poor and often hungry.

One day, their stepmother decided that Hansel and Gretel should go away, as there was not enough food for everyone. Their kind father was very sad but agreed that it must be done. Luckily, Hansel had heard her plan and was prepared.

The next morning, the family went walking in the wood.
They followed lots of different paths that twisted and turned.

Suddenly their stepmother said, "Stay here for a while.
Your father and I are going to collect wood."

Pudsey wants all children to live happily ever after.

The children waited and waited, but their parents never returned. Luckily, clever Hansel had dropped a trail of pebbles along the path, so the children followed them all the way back home.

Their stepmother was very angry when they returned. She locked the door so that Hansel could not collect more pebbles, and the next day she took them much further into the wood before leaving them.

This time, Hansel had dropped a trail of breadcrumbs along the path.
But there were lots of birds in the wood and the breadcrumbs were
soon gone. Hansel and Gretel were lost.
They walked further into the wood until, at last, they came upon a beautiful cottage.

It was made of delicious looking cakes and sweets. A wicked witch lived inside, who
captured the children. She wanted Hansel and Gretel to be her servants.

"Will you show me the fire?" Gretel asked the witch,
"I would like to cook you a delicious meal." She had an idea that
might save them . . .

The witch walked over towards the fire, busy crackling away in the grate.
All at once, Gretel took the pail of water which stood beside it and threw it
over the witch.

The children ran from the cottage and back
through the twisting turning paths of the
wood until they came upon their old house.
Their father was very pleased to
see them, and their stepmother had gone.

The family lived happily ever after in their
little house by the wood.

Witches' Cauldrons

Hubble, bubble, toil and trouble. Try making these savoury treats and selling them.

Ingredients

- **6 small round potatoes**
- **3 tablespoons grated cheddar cheese**
- **2 tablespoons chives, finely chopped**
- **2 tablespoons tinned sweetcorn**
- **2 slices ham, cut into small pieces**
- **6 long thin slices sweet pepper (any colour)**

1. Ask your grown-up helper to preheat the oven to 200C/400F/gas mark 6.

2. Put the potatoes onto a lightly greased baking tray. If they roll about, cut a small piece from the base so they sit firmly.

3. Bake in the oven for about an hour. They are ready when you can easily slide a sharp knife into them. Ask your grown-up helper to do this for you.

4. When they are cool enough to handle, ask your grown-up helper to cut a circle about the size of a large coin from the top.

5. With a teaspoon, carefully scoop the potato out of the skin and into a small mixing bowl. Be careful not to break the skin if you can help it.

6. Add your grated cheese, chives, sweetcorn and ham to the potato and stir well. Scoop the mixture back into the skins.

7. Put your potatoes into a suitable heat-proof container and ask your grown-up helper to place them under a hot grill for about ten minutes, or until the filling is bubbling and turning brown. Don't worry if it starts to spill over the edge. This will make your cauldrons look more witchy!

8. Ask your grown-up helper to remove them from the grill and leave for a few minutes to cool down.

9. Take your strips of pepper and sink the ends of each strip into the sides of the potatoes to make a handle for your cauldron.

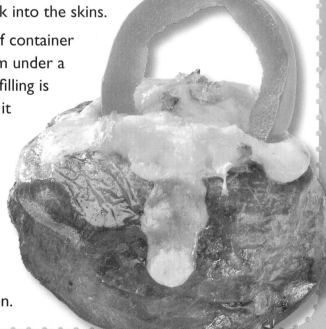

Pizza Shield

Calling all knights and heroes! This recipe for a pizza shield will help you defeat even the most dangerous dragons and the wickedest wizards.

Ingredients

- 200g/7½oz self-raising flour
- 50g/2oz butter or margarine
- 4 tablespoons milk
- 1 tin chopped tomatoes
- 1 cup grated cheese
- ¼ pepper, deseeded and sliced
- 2 mushrooms, cleaned and sliced
- ½ small onion, chopped

1. Ask your grown-up helper to preheat the oven to 220C/425F/gas mark 7.

2. Put the flour into a bowl and rub the butter or margarine into the flour with your hands, until it looks like breadcrumbs.

3. Stir the milk into the mixture. Use a spoon at first, and then use your hands to knead the mixture into a firm dough.

4. Sprinkle a little bit of flour onto a clean surface and roll the dough out flat with a rolling pin.

5. Ask your grown-up helper to cut the dough into a shield shape, and place it on a greased baking tray.

6. Use the spare dough to make two thin sausages and lay these in a cross shape over the shield, to divide it into four sections.

7. Spread the tomatoes evenly over the pizza base. Then sprinkle the cheese all over it. Put your remaining ingredients in each section.

8. Ask your grown-up helper to place the pizza in the oven for fifteen to twenty minutes until the dough has baked, and the cheese is melted and golden.

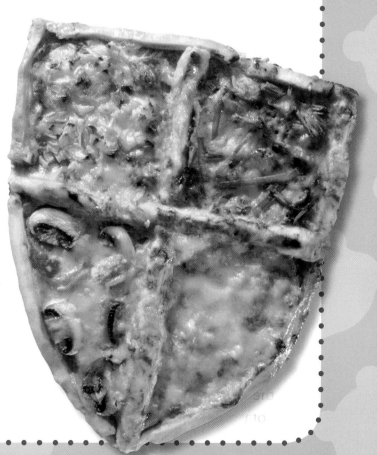

Wear Something Different

Your BBC Children in Need 2009 bandana is a must-have for every Pudsey fan – there are so many things to do with it and ways to wear it – what will you do with yours?

Headband Fold the bandana in half to make a triangle. Then fold it in half so that the pointy tip meets the flat edge. Fold it in half once more so that now you have something that looks like a wide ribbon. Wrap the material around your forehead and tie in a knot at the back of your head.

Hair Band Fold the material as before, and place on top of your head. Turn your head upside down and tie the two ends together at the back of your neck. When you put your head back the right way your hair should fall over the bottom of the bandana.

Pet Accessories Bandana neckerchiefs also look great on your pet dog or cat. But ask your parent or grown-up helper first!

Skull Cap Fold the tip of one of the corners of your bandana in. Then place the bandana on your head with the folded tip just above your eyebrows. Tie the two long ends that are by your ears behind your neck over the third point that is at the back of your head. Make sure you tuck any loose material in.

Neckerchief Fold the bandana into a triangle and tie the two long ends around your neck for a real cowboy look!

Table Cloth A Children in Need bandana is the perfect accessory for an afternoon tea party.

Three-legged Race Mark a starting line and a finish line with some string. Divide everyone into pairs. Use your bandana to tie each pair's ankles. Make sure you don't tie the bandana too tight! The first team to cross the finish line, still tied together, wins!

Pudsey's PJ Party!

Another great way to have fun and raise money for **BBC Children in Need** is to have a pyjama party, or a sponsored sleepover.

You can have sponsored competitions and see who can stay awake the longest or who is the first one to fall asleep.

Everyone can wear their Pudsey pyjamas and you could even hold the sleepover on 20 November to watch the BBC Children in Need Appeal!

Ask a grown-up helper to photocopy this page then cut out the invitation below and colour it in. Then hand it out to all your friends, inviting them to the best sleepover ever!

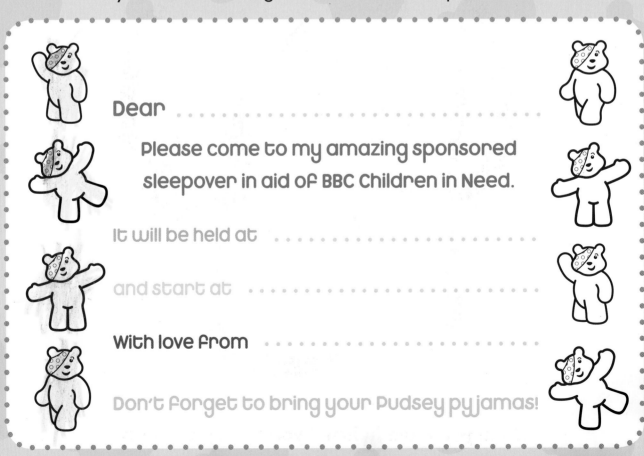

Dear . . . .

Please come to my amazing sponsored sleepover in aid of BBC Children in Need.

It will be held at . . . .

and start at . . . .

With love from . . . .

Don't forget to bring your Pudsey pyjamas!

Dot·to·dot

Who is the picture below of? Join the dots to find out.

Once you have finished you can colour it in.

Sport Something Different

Sports play a big role in **Children in Need** each year, with sports stars and school sports teams all raising a lot of money. You could try some sponsored sports activities yourself.

Football game – get sponsors to donate for each goal scored.

Netball or basketball match – watch the total you raise go up every time the ball goes in the net.

Relay race – raise more money the faster your team's time.

Gymnastics – friends and family could sponsor you to perfect a team routine.

You can raise money without a team too – just you and your friends keeping fit and having fun.

Sponsored cycle – ask friends and family to sponsor you 10p for every metre you cycle!

Football skills – how many times could you bounce a ball, or keep it in the air using your feet?

Swimming – how many lengths of your local swimming pool could you swim?

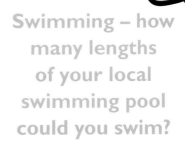

Hula hoop – You could raise more money the more times you hula the hoop!

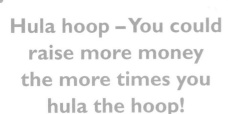

Fly something Different!

Can you make the best paper aeroplane in your class? It's time to put it to the test with a paper plane throwing competition!

Get all your friends to make their best paper aeroplane – are all the designs the same? There are several different ways to make paper planes and some fly better than others.

Make sure everybody has decorated their planes so that you know whose is whose, and then get all the competitors to line up in a straight line, or against a wall, with a large open space in front of them.

The first person in the line should then throw their plane as far as they can. It is not a good idea to get everyone to throw their planes at once as you could end up with several crashes and planes not going as far as they could!

Once the first person's plane has landed, mark the distance it flew and then return the plane to them. This way their plane cannot get pushed forward or backwards by any other planes, making it seem as if they got further, or flew a shorter distance than they really did.

When the last plane has landed have a look at all the markers – a prize should go to the plane that travelled the biggest distance!

To make the day more fun you could also award extra prizes for the best designed or decorated plane or the most unusual plane.

You can use the template on the opposite page to help you get started.

1 Ask a grown-up helper to photocopy this page.
2 Fold the paper in half along the blue line in the centre.
3 Fold down the corners on the red line.
4 Fold down the next section on the orange line on each side.
5 Fold down the last section on the green line on each side.

The Frog Prince

Once there was a princess who lived in a beautiful palace. One day, she wandered into the palace gardens with her favourite plaything, a ball made of gold.

In the garden there was a deep, dark well. The princess sat on the edge of the well and played with the golden ball, throwing it into the air and catching it. After a while, the ball fell through her hands and into the well! The princess began to cry. Suddenly she heard a voice. "Don't cry," it said, "I can find your ball, but what will you do for me in return?" The voice came from a little green frog.

"Oh Mr Froggy," said the princess, "I will give you anything you desire."

"I would like you to let me eat at your table and sleep on your pillow, and I would like you to be my friend," said the frog.

The princess promised, and so the frog hopped into the well and returned the golden ball to her. She was so delighted that she ran back to the palace, leaving the little frog far behind.

The next day at dinner she heard a splishing sploshing noise outside. The frog had come to find her! She didn't want to let him in, but the king said that she had made a promise and she must keep it.

The frog enjoyed a delicious dinner

and then spent a peaceful
night resting on the
princess's pillow.

In the morning the frog was gone, but he returned the
next evening and again ate at the royal table and
slept on the princess's pillow.

The same happened on the third day,
but when the princess awoke at dawn,
it was not a frog that she saw, but a
handsome prince!

"You have broken the spell!" he said.
"An evil witch turned me into a frog
and only the true friendship of a princess
could turn me back into a prince."

The princess was overjoyed and agreed
to marry the handsome prince. The palace
rejoiced and an enormous feast was
prepared to celebrate.

Make a Frog Mask!

Are you a prince in disguise? Make a mask and be the Frog Prince for a fancy dress fundraiser.

You will need:
- tracing paper
- card
- length of elastic
- paints
- paintbrushes
- round-ended scissors
- a grown-up to help you

What to do:

1 Trace the shape of the mask and copy it onto the cardboard. Don't forget the eyes!

2 Ask a grown-up helper to cut out the shape for you, including the eye holes. Make sure the holes are in the right place for you to see out of them!

3 Paint your frog mask bright green and give your frog a cheeky smile!

4 Leave your mask to dry.

5 Ask a grown-up helper to make a hole on each side of the mask.

6 Thread the elastic through the holes. Measure the length so it will hold the mask on your head. Then tie it tightly!

47

Bake a Cake

Baking cakes is always fun to do (especially if you are allowed to lick the bowl!) and it can be a really yummy way to raise money. You could sell the cakes at your next school fundraiser or fête.

Bake For BBC Children in Need

Pudsey Cakes

Ingredients

- 100g/3½ oz soft butter or margarine
- 100g/3½ oz caster sugar
- 2 eggs
- 100g/3½ oz self-raising flour
- paper cake cases
- yellow icing, black icing pens and Smarties or ready to roll icing in yellow or any decorations you'd like

1. Ask your grown-up helper to preheat the oven to 180C/350F/gas mark 4.
2. Mix the butter or margarine and sugar together until creamy with either a wooden spoon or an electric whisk.
3. Crack two eggs into the mixture and beat them in.
4. Hold a sieve over the mixture and pour the flour into it. Gently shake the sieve from side to side, so that the flour falls through the holes and into the mixture. This makes the mixture less lumpy and will make your cakes light and fluffy.
5. Stir the flour into the mixture until it is fairly stiff.
6. Use a teaspoon to dollop the mixture into cake cases. There should be enough for about ten little cakes.
7. Ask your grown-up helper to pop them on a baking tray and place them in the oven for about fifteen minutes. Keep an eye on them to make sure they don't burn. When they are ready, leave them to cool down.
8. Use a spoon to spread the icing or ask your grown-up helper to cut the ready to roll icing into Pudsey shapes.
9. Draw Pudsey's eyes, nose and mouth with the icing pens and decorate his bandana with Smarties. Or be creative and decorate your Pudsey cakes however you like!

Queen of Hearts Tarts

Ingredients

- some flour
- packet shortcrust pasty
- jar of strawberry jam
- a little water

You will also need:
- a circle-shaped cutter
- a heart-shaped cutter

1. Ask your grown-up helper to preheat the oven to 200C/400F/gas mark 6.
2. Lightly grease a baking tray.
3. Sprinkle some flour on to a clean work surface and roll out the pastry.
4. Use the circle-shaped cutter to cut out as many circles as you can.
5. Use the heart-shaped cutter to cut hearts out of the middle of half of the circles.
6. Place the full circles on the greased baking tray and brush the edges of each one with a little water.
7. Place the circles with the hearts cut out over the top.
8. Put a teaspoon of jam in each heart. The jam will spread while cooking, so be careful not to put too much in.
9. Ask your grown-up helper to bake them in the oven for 15-20 minutes, until the pastry is golden.
10. Leave the tarts to cool before serving.

Carrot Cakes

Ingredients

- 100g/3½ oz brown sugar
- 2 eggs
- 1 tablespoon sunflower oil
- 100g/3½ oz self-raising flour
- 2 medium carrots, grated
- 1 cup raisins
- paper cake cases
- 1 tablespoon icing sugar
- 2 tablespoons cream cheese
- orange and green marzipan (optional)

1. Ask your grown-up helper to preheat the oven to 220C/420F/gas mark 7.
2. Put the sugar, eggs and oil into a big bowl. Use an electric whisk or a wooden spoon to mix it until creamy.
3. Fold in the flour.
4. Add the grated carrot and the raisins, and mix with a wooden spoon.
5. Use a teaspoon to fill up your paper cases, and place them on a baking tray. Ask your grown-up helper to put them in the oven for about twenty minutes.
6. Meanwhile, mix the cream cheese with the icing sugar and put it in the fridge for later.
7. If you are using marzipan, make some carrot-shaped decorations.
8. Ask your grown-up helper to remove the cakes from the oven and leave them to cool.
9. Use a spoon to spread the cream cheese icing on top of the cakes, and decorate each with a marzipan carrot.

Cake Sale

where : ....

when : ....

time : ....

Design and colour your own cake sale poster. Pudsey has started it off for you.

Helping in the House

Raising money doesn't have to be something you go out and organise. It is always fun to plan big events and participate in fundraisers, but you can raise money without even leaving the house.

How many times have you heard your mum or dad complain about doing the vacuuming? Or washing the car?

You could offer to do those jobs in exchange for a small donation for Children in Need. There are lots of 'chores' you can offer to do in this way:

- Washing dishes
- Dusting
- Tidying the house
- Washing the car
- Vacuuming
- Laundry
- Cleaning the kitchen or the bathroom
- Painting
- Gardening

Pudsey Maze

Can you help Pudsey's friend find the real Pudsey?
Watch out for the Pudsey bears in costume.

Dressing Up

Pudsey loves to wear costumes and play dress-up.
Design a costume for Pudsey.

Show and Dance

**Are you an aspiring actor or a drama queen?
A guitar hero or a dancing diva? If so, then why not
share your talents to help BBC Children in Need?**

Your band could perform
a concert to raise money.
Tie Pudsey bandana's to your
instruments. Make posters
advertising your BBC Children
in Need concert.
You could learn this year's BBC
Children in Need song.

You could put on a play with
your friends or drama troupe.
See if you can use the Pudsey
bandana or pyjamas as part of
your costumes, or the Pudsey
mug or shopping bag as props.
You could sell tickets to your
performance to raise money.

Perform a dance show with your friends or dance club. Make sure you practise your routine really well. Watch Strictly Come Dancing for ideas. You could even have some of your friends or family acting as judges. Can you do as well as Terry and Tess did last year?

If you and your friends sing, dance, act or play music, you could put on a variety show! Create a timetable of who is performing when, so that you break up similar acts. Will your variety show be as good as the BBC Children in Need appeal?

Whatever show you decide to hold, you are going to need a programme for it. Photocopy the template on the back of this page, remembering to cover up the grey instructions, and then use that to help you design your programme.

Create a programme for your BBC Children in Need fundraiser show.

If you have room you could include a piece on the
story behind your dance or play.

Write a piece telling your audience about the acts.

Write a list of the events taking place and the times
they will be on.

Tonight's
Entertainment

Welcome to

All proceeds go to
BBC Children in Need

Write the name of your show and put the date.

How many Pudseys?

**Guess how many Pudseys are on this page.
Get your friends and family to guess too. Then count
them all carefully and see who was closest. The answer
is at the bottom of the page.**

You could use this game as a fundraising idea too. Fill a jar with small sweets and
get people to donate to BBC Children in Need to guess the number of sweets.

Once you have counted the sweets in the jar, whoever guessed the closest
amount wins the sweets!

Answer: 26

Pudsey's Friends

Photographed by MJ Kim

Marc

What is your favourite thing about BBC Children in Need? My favourite thing about BBC Children in Need is that you can do fun things, while you're really helping people.

Sam

How would you raise money for BBC Children in Need? I love to cook, so I'd spend a week cooking a three-course meal every night for my friends, and charge them on the door.

McFly

BBC Children in Need has been really fantastic. We met some children who lost their mum this year. Children in Need has supported them and made a huge difference to their lives. Pudsey does so much for kids out there who need help.

Tom Daley

If you and Pudsey could spend the afternoon together, what would you do? I would teach him to dive!

DUFFY

As a little girl I used to go to school, once a year, wearing a non school uniform outfit to raise money and now I have had a chance to perform on the show - it's great!

Photographed by John Wright for Radio Times Magazine.

Richard Hammond

How would you raise money for BBC Children in Need?
I would have to do something energetic, so some sort of sponsored thing. I'm not really much good at any of the things I'd want to do, so best make them silly. A sponsored scared of heights rock climb could be good or a sponsored run through custard!

Fearne Cotton

Why is it important to support BBC Children in Need?
There are so many kids out there who don't get a fair deal. Kids should be out having fun and being carefree, BUT there are so many who have to worry about illness, loss of parents, domestic abuse, or social situations. BBC Children in Need helps so many kids have a better quality of life and gives them the chance to be KIDS!!

Where Your Money Goes

Helping Children Like These

Pudsey helps children who are disabled, have a learning disability and those who find it difficult to speak. For children who have a disability, going to school can be very scary and they can feel alone and upset.

Learning to build with blocks.

Pudsey doesn't think any child should feel left out because of their disability, which is why **BBC Children in Need** gives grants to places like **Kid City**. At Kid City, small children can get the support they need to be ready for nursery.

Pudsey learns some new words from Latasha and the kids.

Mark loves the slide!

Arts and crafts time!

Latasha is a teacher at Kid City. She gives each child the help they need to get ready for school. Together, they learn how to speak in different ways. She even teaches them sign language, a special language of hand gestures and movements for deaf children. This way, no one feels left out!

Anna and Pudsey are best friends.

Pudsey gets a bath in oats!

Kid City makes every child feel special. At the end of every day, Latasha says, "Everyone leaves smiling!"

Every child deserves to be happy, and with Pudsey's help, Kid City can make sure to give these children the skills they need to be ready and excited for school!

Now that's something to smile about!

There are always happy faces at Kid City!

Pudsey's Tips

Ready?

❶ Visit www.bbc.co.uk/pudsey
<http://www.bbc.co.uk/pudsey>

❷ Call 0345 607 33 33 for your fundraiser pack or download it from Pudsey's website.

❸ Do Something Different.

❹ Be safe.

❺ Tell us about it. Let us know what you're planning this year.

❻ Pay in your money as soon as possible so we can add it to the grand total!

❼ Watch the show on Friday, 20 November.

❽ Have fun!